# SEA...

**This book belongs to:**

I began this book on: (DATE)

I made my first I-Spy on: (DATE)

I sent off for my badge on: (DATE)

To get you started on the 1000 points you need for a badge, here are a few easy spots you can make now.

In the 'Power of the Sea and Safety' what does the flag look like that indicates the 'Swimming Area'?
**5 points for a right answer**

In 'Life on the Rocks', what resembles a paint splash?
**5 points for a right answer**

How many common periwinkles can you see in 'Life on the Rocks'?
**5 points for a right answer**

In 'Life under Rocks and Stones' how many arms does the brittle star have?
**5 points for a right answer**

*Answers on page 48*

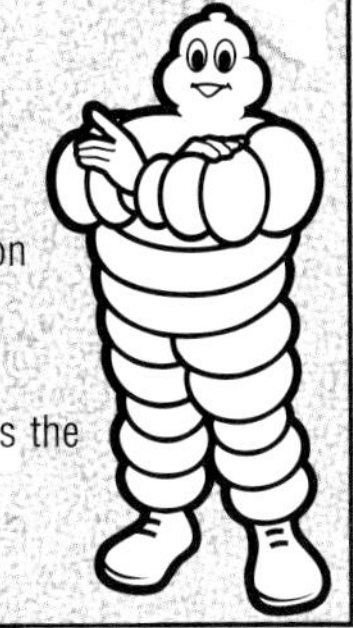

# POWER OF THE SEA AND SAFETY

The sea is one of the most powerful and potentially dangerous forces in nature. Just think of waves, currents, and tides. In winter, an Atlantic wave can exert a pressure of more than 9000 kilograms per square metre and, during storms, at least three times as much! And, in the Bristol Channel, for example, currents may reach speeds of 10 knots during a spring tide when the water may rise as much as 12 metres. **Treat the sea with respect and take note of the warning about tides in the introduction. Estuaries, too, can be dangerous places where there are deep, sucking mud or quicksands and currents that can be treacherous and run fast as they swirl among the channels.**

**Beach warning notice**
Although a beach may look perfectly safe, there may be strong currents offshore that make it dangerous at times. This notice tells bathers and surfers to obey the flag signals so that they can enjoy themselves in safety. ☐
*I-Spy for **10***

**Beach warning flag**
Many beaches today are equipped with sets of flags showing holidaymakers which areas of beach can be used for swimming, which can be used for surfing, and which can be used for boats. This, of course, makes the beach safer and more enjoyable for everyone. ☐
*I-Spy for **10***

**Beach lifeguard**
On beaches where there are good waves, especially along our western coasts, surfing is becoming more and more popular. Occasionally surfers may get into difficulties and local councils therefore employ lifeguards to keep an eye on the situation.
*I-Spy for **20** – double if the lifeguard also has a boat* ☐

**Surfer**
Surfing is now a very popular pastime and you will see surfers enjoying themselves on any sandy shore where there are good waves rolling in from deeper waters.
*I-Spy for **10***

**Groyne**
You will usually find groynes on sandy or pebbly shores. They are there to reduce the currents running along the coastline which would otherwise wash away the sand or shingle from the beach.
*I-Spy for **10***

**Lighthouse**
Lighthouses are intended, of course, to show shipping the positions of any dangerous parts of the coastline. Today, nearly all lighthouses run automatically and the lighthouse-keeper is an occupation of the past.
*I-Spy for **10***
*Double if you are able to go safely to the top of the lighthouse*

# BEACHCOMBING AND POLLUTION

In many parts of the world, beaches have become polluted with all sorts of debris in the past few decades: plastic bottles, metal cans, human waste, oil, tar, even supermarket trolleys. This can make lovely beaches dirty and dangerous places for humans and wildlife alike. In various parts of the world, governments have tried to bring in laws to make the beaches in their countries, cleaner, safer, and pleasanter places for visitors and to provide good habitats for animals and plants. But, because the seas are so vast and their power to transport detritus is so great, it is hard for national laws to be totally effective. It has been suggested, for example, that much of the beach waste on the western shores of Britain comes across the Atlantic from the United States! But some of the natural flotsam and jetsam cast up on our shores can be fascinating . . .

**Tyred out!**
As well as bits of rope and seaweed on the groyne, you can see that an old tyre has been washed up on the beach, trapped by the groyne, and partly buried in sand. Used tyres, of course, make useful fenders to protect the sides of boats. Perhaps this one came adrift . . . ☐
*I-Spy for* ***10***

**Ropes and nets**
Fishing is an important industry that provides the world with a lot of valuable food. Inevitably, ropes and nets become snagged and torn and are carried off by the sea. Modern materials, such as terylene and nylon, do not decompose as quickly as the old hempen ropes, and remnants are often washed up on beaches . . . ☐
*I-Spy for* ***10***

. . . and, as well as rope, nere is the remains of a obster pot that must have oeen broken away from its mooring by currents, or oerhaps lost from a small obster fishing boat in rough seas.
*I-Spy for **10***

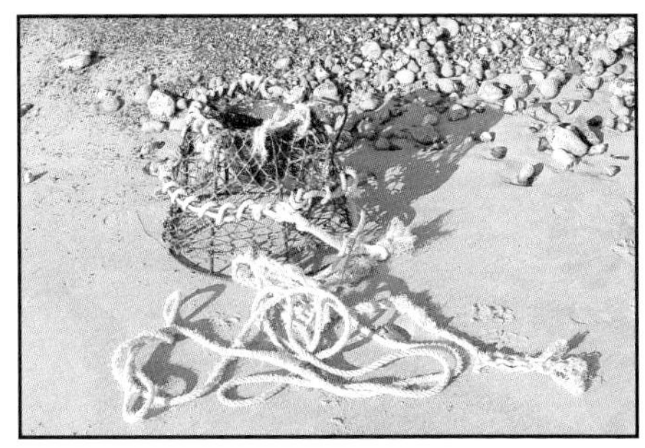

**Net weight**
A trawler fishing net is a bit like a bag towed behind the fishing boat into a shoal of fish. The mouth of the net is kept open by boards, floats hold it up, and weights like iron rollers hold the net on the seabed. Here is a weight that must have broken away from a net.
*I-Spy for **20** for a float and **100** for a weight like this one*

**Piling shoe**
Here's a rare one. This post is all that remains of some old sea defences. The pointed metal device on the top is called a piling shoe. When sea defences are wrecked by the power of the sea, bits of bulk timber may be left behind or washed up.
*I-Spy **10** for bulk timber, **100** for a piling shoe*

**Pebbles on the beach**

It goes without saying that a pebble beach is made up of pebbles, but what are the pebbles composed of? Here is a pebble of chalk (the white one) and one of brick. Both have been rounded and drilled by the sea rolling them back and forth . . .

*I-Spy **15** each for a chalk and a brick pebble*

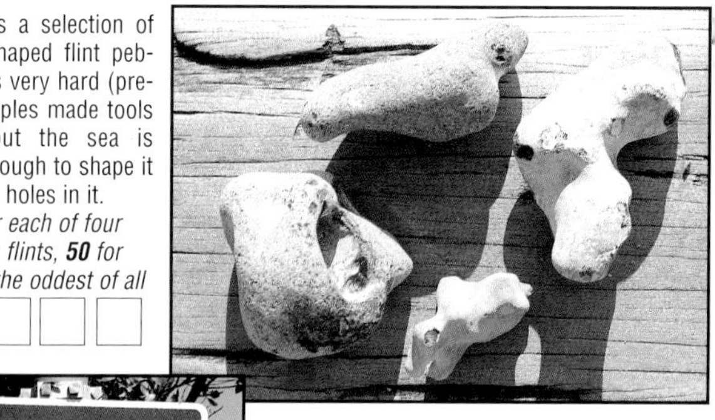

. . . here's a selection of strangely shaped flint pebbles. Flint is very hard (prehistoric peoples made tools from it) but the sea is powerful enough to shape it or even drill holes in it.

*I-Spy **10** for each of four odd-looking flints, **50** for one that is the oddest of all*

IMPORTANT NOTICE FOR DOG OWNERS
North Cornwall District Council
Cornwall County Council Act 1984
Section 9
DOGS ARE PROHIBITED ON THIS BEACH BETWEEN EASTER DAY & 1st OF OCTOBER IN EACH YEAR
This ban does not apply to dogs kept and used solely by blind persons for guidance.
Any person being in charge of a dog who permits the dog to go or remain on the beach during the above period shall be guilty of an offence with a maximum fine of £400.

**No dogs!**

During the winter months, when there are few holidaymakers, it is nice for dogs to be able to run on the beach. In the summer, however, when lots of children play on the beach it is better to keep it clean for them. Look out for this notice informing owners when their dogs can use the beach.

*I-Spy for **10***

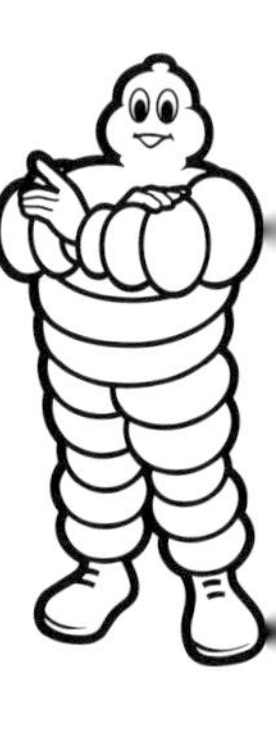

**Rocky shore**
Much of the shoreline around our coasts is rocky. On these shores you will usually find lots of rock pools containing a wealth of winkles, prawns, crabs, fishes, and many other creatures. Growing on the rocks you will find different kinds of seaweeds as well as animals such as barnacles and limpets.
*I-Spy for **10***

**Sandy shore**
This is just the sort of shore on which to build sandcastles but it is not as rich in animals and seaweeds as a rocky shore. Look out, though, for animals that live beneath the sand, such as the sea potato and the lug worm.
*I-Spy for **10***

**Stone and shingle beach**
Very few animals and plants are to be found on a beach like this because the action of the waves constantly rolling the pebbles around prevents them from living their normal lives. Look out for the animal remains that may get washed up on them.
*I-Spy for **10***

**Muddy shore**
This kind of shore may be found along estuaries where our rivers enter the sea. It is not wise to venture out on to the mud because it is all too easy to become trapped in the ooze. Look out from the top of the shore and you will see many different kinds of waders and other birds feeding on the tiny animals that live in the mud.
*I-Spy for **10** Double if you also see a rainbow*

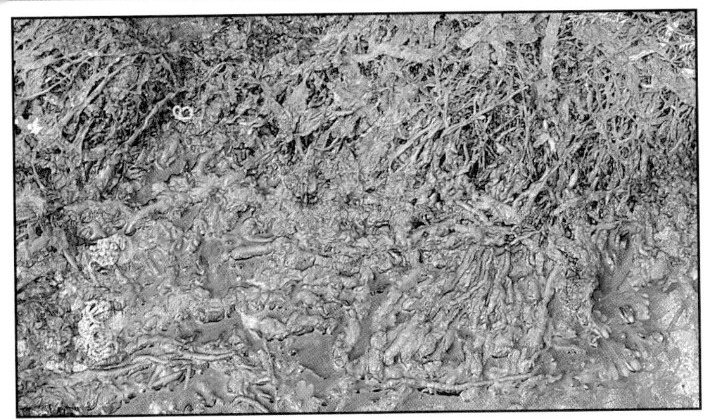

**Gutweed**
This is a very common green seaweed, usually found at the top of the shore attached to the rocks. It gets its common name because, in shape, it rather resembles the intestines of an animal.
*I-Spy for **10***

**Sea lettuce**
It is easy to see how this seaweed gets its name, for its fronds look like the limp leaves of a wilting lettuce. Look for it on rocks on the middle part of the shore.
*I-Spy for **10***

**Jelly buttons**

You may find it hard to believe that this is not just a blob of jelly but it really is a living thing, and is one of the brown seaweeds. You may also find it growing attached to other seaweeds as well as on rocks.

*I-Spy for* ***15***

**Oarweed**

Sometimes also called kelp, you will see this brown seaweed exposed only at very low tides when it sticks up out of the water as it is in the photograph. It is, however, often washed up in large amounts at the top of the shore after winter storms.

*I-Spy for* ***15***

**A holdfast**
Most seaweeds attach themselves to the rocks on which they live by means of a holdfast. This is an oar-weed holdfast. It looks a bit like the roots of a land plant. The tangled branches of the holdfast are home for many small shore animals.
*I-Spy for **15***

**Thongweed**
Although it looks a bit like a mushroom, this is actually another brown seaweed, and is usually found on the lower shore. During the summer, the long fronds, 'thongs', grow from the centre of the button and it is from these that the plant gets its name.
*I-Spy **10** for the button and **10** for the thongs*

**Knotted wrack**

This brown seaweed is very common on the middle shore. It gets its name from the long fronds, with their air bladders at intervals, that resemble knots along a rope. These egg-shaped sacs are floats and give the plant its alternative name of egg wrack.

*I-Spy for* ***10***

**Bladder wrack**

Bladder wrack is much more flattened than knotted wrack, and its air bladders are usually in pairs. It is very common on rocks on the middle shore.

*I-Spy for* ***10***

**Saw wrack**

This seaweed grows at the bottom of the shore below the other common wracks. It is easily recognizable for it lacks bladders and the edges of the fronds are toothed like the blade of a saw.

*I-Spy for **10***

**Red rags**

This bright-red seaweed has very thick, tough fronds that, as the common name suggests, hang from the rocks of the lower shore like bundles of rags.

*I-Spy for **20***

**Red encrusting seaweeds**
It may surprise you to discover that the red or pink 'paint splashes' over the surfaces of the rocks on the middle and lower shore are actually red seaweeds. Some are perfectly smooth while others are knobbly.
*I-Spy for* ***15***

**Dulse**
Dulse grows together with red rags but the fronds are less brightly coloured and much thinner. This is one of the edible seaweeds, though not much use is made of it these days.
*I-Spy for* ***10***

**Epiphytic red seaweed**
This little red seaweed is common on most shores where it is found 'hitching a ride' up towards the sunlight by growing on the fronds of the much bigger weed, knotted wrack ('epiphytic' describes a plant that uses another plant for physical support).
*I-Spy for **10***

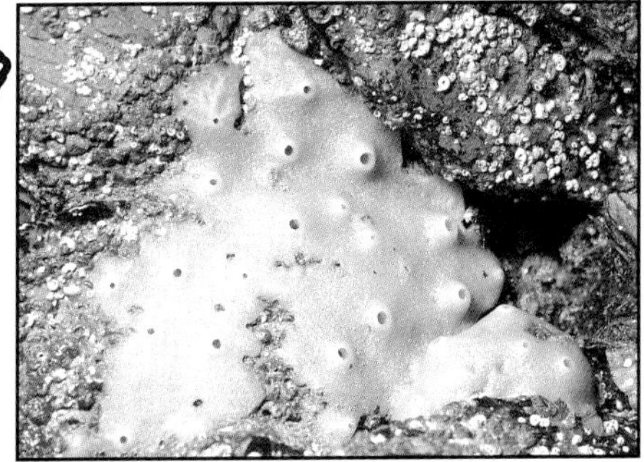

**Breadcrumb sponge**
This is the commonest and most easily recognized of the sponges that grow around our coastline. It grows in thin sheets across the surfaces of rocks, usually on the undersides. It may be yellow through to pale orange or green in colour. Look for it lower down the shore. Are sponges animals or plants?

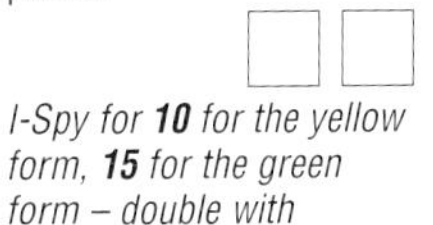

*I-Spy for **10** for the yellow form, **15** for the green form – double with answer*

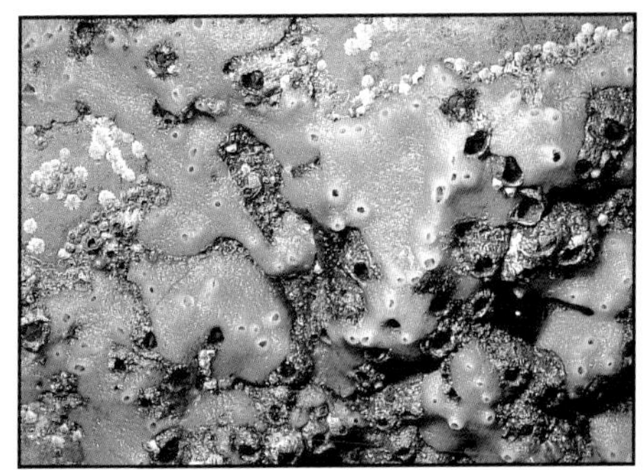

**Orange encrusting sponge**

This sponge lives in the same sort of place as the breadcrumb sponge but it is less common. It also has a more folded surface and does not have the little volcano-shaped humps sticking out from it.

*I-Spy for* ***20***

**Greenleaf worm**

This little green worm may often be found crawling around on the surface of wet rocks as the tide goes out. Usually just a few are to be found but sometimes it occurs in very large numbers.

*I-Spy for* ***15***

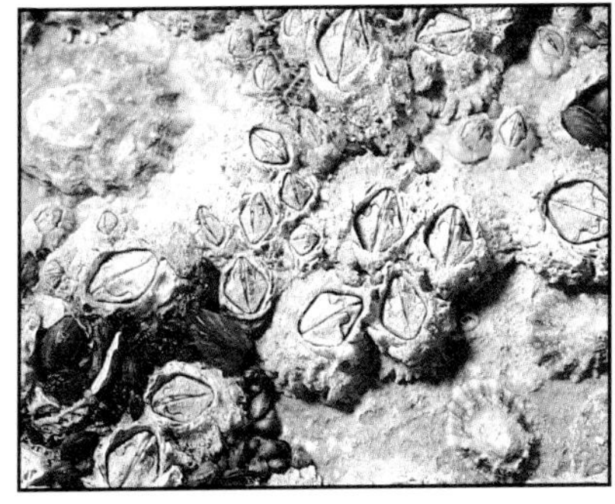

**Acorn barnacles**
People sometimes find it hard to believe that these are not relatives of limpets and winkles. They are, in fact, crustaceans and are related to crabs and lobsters. The white plates protect the animal within. The four plates at the top open to allow the animal to kick its legs in the water to take in particles of food. It is very common on all rocky shores.
*I-Spy for **10***

**Chiton or coat-of-mail shell**
Although it looks a bit like a woodlouse, the chiton is actually related to limpets and winkles, that is, it is a mollusc. Instead of having a single shell, it is covered by a series of plates and, if the chiton is dislodged from the surface of the rock, it can roll up to protect itself.
*I-Spy for **10** for a normal grey or green one*
*Double for a pink one*

**Common limpet**

The limpet is one of the most familiar animals on the rocky shore. It can hold on to a rock very tightly and is not easy to dislodge. After feeding over the surfaces of the rocks on which it lives, a limpet often returns to favourite spot where, after a time, its shell may make a deep groove in the rock.

*I-Spy for* ***10***

**Blue-rayed limpet**
This pretty little limpet is much smaller than the common limpet and has a curved, rather than pointed, shell. You will find them only during those days when the tides are very low, usually on the stems or fronds of oarweed *(see page 10)*.
*I-Spy for* ***10***

**Flat topshell**
With their purple lines on a greenish background, flat topshells are quite colourful. The top of the shell is often worn away to reveal the silvery 'mother-of-pearl' beneath. They are common on the middle shore.
*I-Spy for* ***10***

**Painted topshell**
You will have to search among the fronds of seaweed and under overhanging rocks during very low tides to find this attractively marked topshell. Unlike other topshells, which often occur in large numbers, it is usually found singly or in twos.
*I-Spy for **10***

**Common periwinkle**
When the tide is out, you will find this animal hanging beneath rocks and stones, often in large numbers. If you are lucky, you may find some crawling around actively in a rock pool. This is the famous edible winkle and is collected for humans to eat.
*I-Spy for **10***
*Double if you see someone collecting them for food*

**Flat periwinkle**
The flat periwinkle is not really flat at all but the shell does not have a point on it like that of the common periwinkle. Flat periwinkles may be black, green, yellow, or orange, and are often found crawling around over bladder wrack fronds.
*I-Spy for **10***

**Spotted cowrie**
Most people associate cowries with tropical seas but we do have some small ones around our shores. To find the spotted cowrie you will have to search under rock overhangs right down at the bottom of the shore during very low tides.
*I-Spy for **20***

**Dog whelk**
The dog whelk is one of the commonest creatures on the shore, and is always found with the barnacles and mussels on which it feeds. As you can see, its shell colour and pattern are very variable. In summer you will find them with their yellow/pink, flask-shaped egg capsules.
*I-Spy for* ***10***
*Double if you find them with egg capsules*

**Sea-hare**
Look out for this sea-slug as it crawls around on seaweeds, especially in spring when it can sometimes be found in large numbers. It is called the 'sea-hare' because of the long, ear-like projections on its head.
*I-Spy for* ***15***

**Sea-lemon**
You may find this sea-slug on the undersides of rocks and stones lower down the shore and sometimes in rock pools. Look out for the mass of feathery gills on its tail end. Its colour and texture are similar to the skin of a lemon.
*I-Spy for* ***15***

**Common grey sea-slug**
Like the other sea-slugs, you will find this one under rocks or on weeds. In water, as in the picture, it is very attractive to look at but out of water it looks like an untidy blob of grey jelly. Look out, too, for its strands of pink eggs.
*I-Spy for* ***15***

**Common mussel**
Mussels may be found in very large numbers on rocks on the middle shore, so much so that they leave no room between them for anything else to settle down. Each mussel attaches itself to the rock by special threads called a byssus.
*I-Spy for* ***10***

**Cushion star**
This is our only common short-armed starfish. It is found on rocks, beneath stones, and among weeds, mainly along our southern and western coasts.
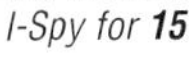
*I-Spy for* ***15***

**Common starfish**
The common starfish is well named for, at times, it can be found in quite large numbers. It lives all round our coasts and is usually to be found beneath rock overhangs and boulders when the tide is out. If a starfish loses one or more arms it can grow them again. True or false?

*I-Spy for **10***
*Double with answer*

**Common sea urchin**
The common sea urchin is not really as numerous as its name suggests. This is mainly because people collect the tests (shell-like skeletons) to use as ornaments. You will have to look for it under rocks at the very bottom of the shore during our lowest tides.
*I-Spy for **20***

**;ea-mat**
'here is a number of different kinds of sea-mat, hough they all look similar o the naked eye. They are nost commonly found on he lower shore, mainly on eaweed fronds but also ttached to rocks.
*'-Spy for **15***

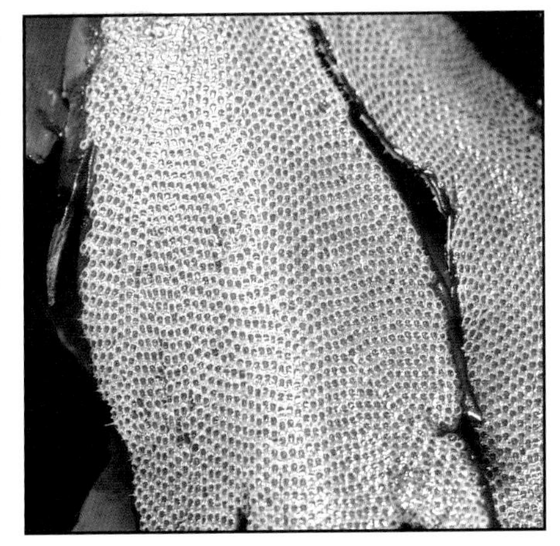

**Light-bulb sea squirt**
Sea squirts are so-called because, when you touch one out of water, it contracts and shoots a stream of water out of its mouth. The light-bulb sea squirt is found under rock overhangs on the lower shore.
*I-Spy for **15***

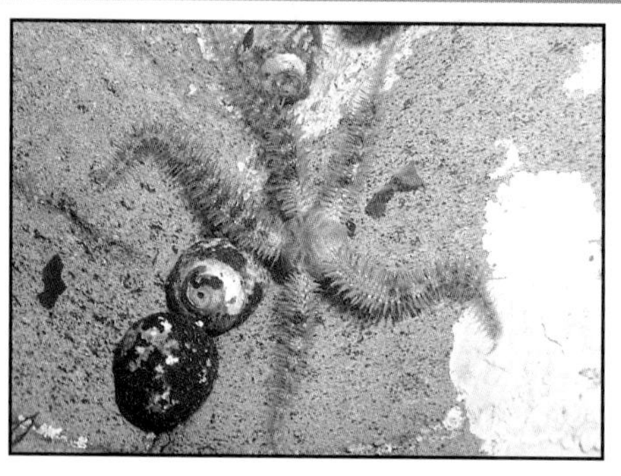

**Brittle star**
These relatives of th starfish are quite small bu may be found in quite larg numbers living beneat stones on the lower shore Be careful with them fo they are quite brittle an their arms will break off they are handled carelessly.
*I-Spy for **10***

**Green sea urchin**
This is our commonest sea urchin and you will find them clinging to the undersides of large stones and rocks all around our coastline. It often camouflages itself by holding on to bits of seaweed and shell by means of its sucker feet.
*I-Spy for **10***
*Double if you find one with shell and weed covering its body*

**Squat lobster**
The squat lobster resembles the much larger edible lobster in appearance but i is much smaller and the pincers on the front legs are only very small. It can be very common under stones on the lower shore.
*I-Spy for **15***

**road-clawed porcelain rab**

ou will usually find this rab, often in good num-ers, hanging tightly to the ndersides of stones on he lower shore. When you urn the stone over, they vill either drop off or scut-le around to what is now he underside of the tone.

*-Spy for* ***10***

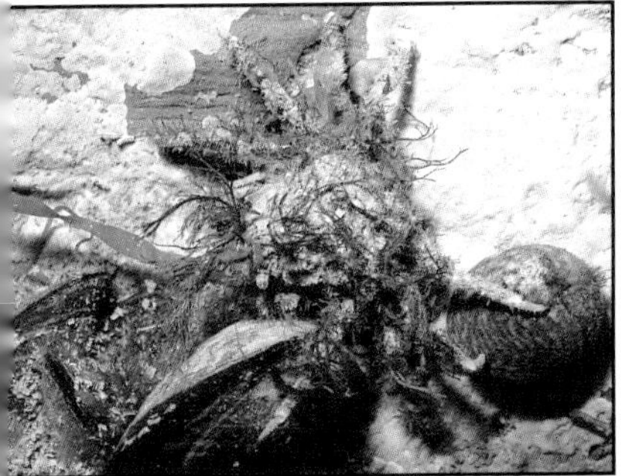

**Spider crab**

Spider crabs are so-called because they have rather small bodies and long, thin arms. Some species, which live in deeper water, grow quite large but this is only a small one. Though not uncommon, the spider crab is not easy to find because it camouflages itself with bits of weed, as the one in the picture has done.

*I-Spy for* ***15***

**Edible crab**

You will usually find smaller crabs of this type under stones on the shore – the further down you are the more common they become. Bigger individuals will usually be found in clefts in the rocks or below the low-tide line. Be careful if you pick one up! They have very powerful pincers.

*I-Spy for* ***10***

**Swimming crab**
This is a rather nicel marked crab which ca become quite large. It ma be very aggressive and ha very powerful pincers. It i more often found along ou southern and wester coasts. Can you see fror the picture why it is called swimming crab?

*I-Spy for **10***
*Double with answer*

**Shore crab**
This is our commonest crab, found on all types of shore and often a long way up into estuaries. It is variable in colour and older individuals may often have barnacles on the shell.
*I-Spy for **5***

**Moulting shore crab**
All crabs and lobsters grow by shedding their old skins every now and then. In the photograph, there are not two crabs but one that has just changed its skin and swollen to its new size before the skin hardens. Note how much it has been able to expand.
*I-Spy for **20***

**Keelworm tubes**

Keelworms live in tubes, attached to rocks and the undersides of stones, that they make from a chalky material. If you put the stone with the tubes on into a rock pool and watch, you may see the worm stick its head out of the tube. Do not forget to put the stone back where you got it from.

*I-Spy for* ***10***

*Double if you persuade the worm to put its head out*

**Worm pipe fish**

Found around all our coasts, though more common in the south-west, this is perhaps the commonest of our pipe fishes. You can sometimes find two or three together under the same stone on the lower shore.

*I-Spy for* ***20***

**Shore clingfish**

You will find this interesting little fish only along our western coasts. It is found lower down the shore, often in good numbers. It has suckers on the underside allowing it to cling on to rocks and stones.

*I-Spy for* ***20***

**Rock pools**
Rock pools are usually absolutely brimming with seaweeds, prawns, small fishes, and many other creatures. Be very careful when investigating them however, for some pools can be quite deep.
*I-Spy for **5***

**Japweed**
In recent years a number of alien seaweeds have been introduced to our coasts, carried on the bottoms of ships returning from far-off places. Japweed is one of them. It was brought in on oysters from the Pacific Ocean and is now spreading around our coasts.
*I-Spy for **10***

**Tamarisk-weed**
You are most likely to come across this interesting seaweed in lower-shore pools around the south-west coasts of Britain. In some lights it is just a normal brown seaweed but, when the sun reflects from it, it seems to change colour to the blue-green shown here.
*I-Spy for **15***

**Sea oak**
This brown seaweed does look a bit like miniature oak trees covered in acorns. It is to be found in deeper pools on the lower shore around our south-western coasts.
*I-Spy for* ***15***

**Coral-weed**
This is one of our commonest red seaweeds and is found in large quantities in middle-shore rock pools all around the coast. It is very hard to the touch because it has a chalky skeleton, and you will often find the skeleton washed up intact after the plant has died.
*I-Spy for* ***5***

**Beadlet anemone**
This is by far the commonest of our sea anemones and lives on rocks over much of the shore. You may find it with its tentacles extended, as here, when it is in a pool or, just as often, as a blob of jelly hanging from a rock out of water.
*I-Spy for* ***10***

**Strawberry anemone**

This anemone is well named for, in colour and pattern, it does look like a strawberry. It is found all around our coasts, usually under rocks towards the bottom of the shore. It can be quite common.

*I-Spy for* ***15***

**Snakelocks anemone**

This anemone comes in two colour forms, with grey or green tentacles with pink tips. It normally pushes its body into cracks in the bottoms of the pools in which it lives. How do the tentacles of this anemone differ from those of the beadlet and strawberry anemones?

*I-Spy for* ***15***
*Double with answer*

**Common prawn**
The common prawn really is common and may be found swimming around in pools on the upper and middle shores, often in large numbers. Although it is very transparent, if you look carefully you will see that it also has some colourful spots and markings on it.
*I-Spy for* ***5***

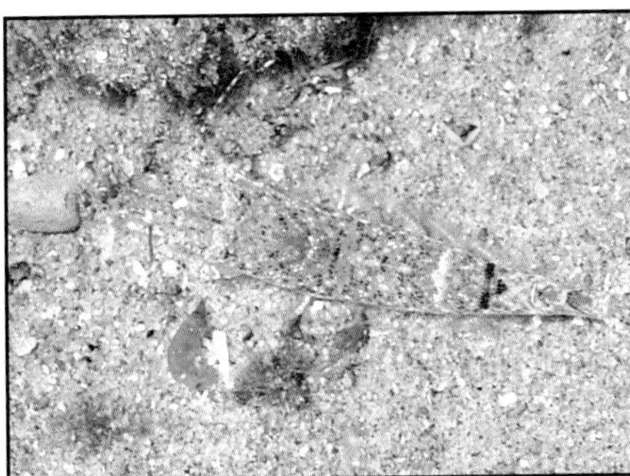

**Brown or edible shrimp**
You are much more likely to find this animal in pools with sandy bottoms where, like the one in the photograph, it is able to camouflage itself by changing its pattern to match that of the sand. This makes the shrimp very difficult to spot.
*I-Spy for* ***15***

**Hermit crab**
Hermit crabs do not have a protective carapace like other crabs but instead they push their soft bodies into old winkle and dog whelk shells for protection. As they grow, they change shells to suit their size.
*I-Spy for* ***10***

**Spiny starfish**
This big, greyish starfish is covered with dull-tipped spines and is usually found on the lower shore in deeper pools or beneath large rocks and stones. It is restricted to our southern and western coasts.
*I-Spy for **20***

**Sea-spider**
Despite the fact that they have four pairs of legs, sea-spiders are not closely related to the familiar land spiders. Although they are not uncommon, sea-spiders are not easy to find because, when the tide is out, they tend to hide in tangles of seaweed and among seaweed holdfasts.
*I-Spy for **20***

**Rockpool springtail**
Springtails have three pairs of legs and are close relatives of insects. The rockpool springtail is about 3 mm long and is quite common. It is usually found floating on the surface of rock pools, often in large groups, or running around on the surfaces of rocks.
*I-Spy for **15***

### Dab

The dab is a flatfish, related to the plaice, and young fishes may often be found scooting around on the beds of sandy-bottomed pools. They are not easy to pick out because they are able to change their colours to match the colour of the sand, in which they also partly bury themselves.

*I-Spy for **15***

### Lesser sand eel

These little fishes are usually to be found in sandy-bottomed pools, around the bases of large rocks which provide hiding places. They may be found in fairly dense shoals in these places and are an important source of food for puffins and other fish-eating birds.

*I-Spy for **15***

### Common blenny

This is a very common little fish all around our coasts. It is found in rock pools over most of the shore and often sits in full view, scuttling away to hide among the weed or under stones only when it notices your presence. Another name for this fish is the shanny. True or false?

*I-Spy for **10***
*Double with answer*

**Butterfish**

Look for this long, rather eel-like fish under stones in pools towards the bottom of the shore. It is easily recognizable by its shape and by the row of dark blotches along the centre of its back.

*I-Spy for **15***

**Father lasher**

The father lasher resembles, and is related to, the bullhead that lives in freshwater streams. It is rather spiny, so should not be picked up, and its colouring makes it rather difficult to spot as it lies on the bottom of the pool among stones or weed.

*I-Spy for **15***

**Cliffs**
Towering cliffs are a common sight along much of our coastline, especially in the north and west. They are important nesting sites for many of our seabirds, such as gulls, gannets, and fulmars.
*I-Spy for **10***
*Double if there are birds nesting on your cliffs*

**Sea cave**
Caves are usually most abundant in cliffs where the rock is relatively soft, though this is not always the case. Where the sea enters the cave it may be used by grey seal females as a place to produce their pups and keep them hidden until they are ready to go to sea.
*I-Spy for **20***

**Sand dunes**
Dunes are formed when strong winds blowing from the sea heap the sand up, and this is then held in place by the plants that begin to grow on it. Sand dunes are very important habitats for animals and plants to live in and should be treated with respect.
*I-Spy for **10***

**Yellow splash lichen**
Above the high-tide line, in what is called the splash zone, the rocks often look as if they have been splashed with patches of yellow paint. These patches are, however, yellow splash lichen which, when young, is roughly circular, as shown in the photograph, but as it gets older becomes more irregular in shape.
*I-Spy for* ***5***

**Sea ivory lichen**
Like the yellow splash lichen, sea ivory is widespread and often grows with it. The 'stems' are very stiff and the flat-topped ones are the lichen's 'fruiting bodies'.
*I-Spy for* ***10***

**Sea-slater**
Looking for all the world like a rather large wood-louse, which is a fairly close relative, the sea-slater may be found scuttling around on and under rocks at the top of the shore and above the high-tide line. It is very common.
*I-Spy for* ***10***

**Sandhopper**
This common species is one of a number of different sandhoppers that share a common life-style. They live, often in very large numbers, among stones, washed-up seaweeds, and in burrows in the sand at the top of the shore and above the high-tide line.
*I-Spy for* ***5***

**Shore bristletail**
Bristletails are very primitive, wingless insects. This species is common along most shore-lines and lives above the high-tide line on cliffs, among rocks and boulders, and in similar places. They have the ability to jump to escape from danger and you will sometimes find them forming quite large groups.
*I-Spy for* ***15***

**Sea-worn pebbles**
Examining the pebbles on the shore can be quite rewarding because they show us samples of the kinds of rocks that are to be found along a particular part of the coast Smooth pebbles usually indicate a soft rock whereas rougher ones are usually from a harder rock.
*I-Spy for **5***

**The strand line**
The strand line is the name we give to the line of debris, at the top of the shore, which has been deposited by the incoming tide. It may contain shells, old crab skins, seaweed feathers, and, unfortunately, all sorts of rubbish produced by humans.
*I-Spy for **5***

**Lugworm**

The lugworm lives beneath the sand on sandy beaches and along estuaries. You will not see the worm itself unless you dig it up, though you may see one if you find someone digging them up for fishing bait. In the photograph, the depression in the sand is above the worm's head and the spirals of sand show where the end of its body lies.

*I-Spy for **10** – double if you see a lugworm dug up as bait*

**Sand mason worm**

The sand mason worm does not live free in the sand but makes a tube from particles of sand which the worm glues together. What you will find, resembling little trees sticking out of the sand, are the ends of these tubes from which the worm sticks out its head to feed when the tide is in.

*I-Spy for **15***

**Honeycomb worm**

You will have to search for the 'reefs' of the honeycomb worm at low tide on shores where rocks give way to sand. The worm builds its sand tubes over the surfaces of the rocks, sometimes covering large areas.

*I-Spy for **15***

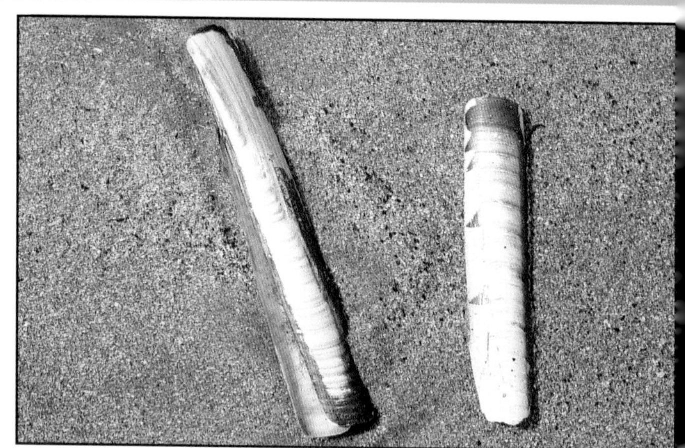

**Razor shell**
Razor shells are molluscs related to mussels and cockles. They normally live buried in sand, sticking out their head ends to feed when the tide is in. You will rarely find the living animal but their shells are often found lying around on a sandy shore.
*I-Spy for **10***

**Cockles and tellins**
Cockles (the bigger shell), which we eat, and tellins (the small shells) live buried in the sand and form an important source of food for birds such as the oystercatcher. Usually you will find the shells of the dead animals but occasionally you may find a living individual stranded by the falling tide before it could bury itself in the sand.
*I-Spy for **10** – double for finding a live one in its shell*

**Scallop**

Scallop shells are commonly washed up on to the shore from the deeper water where most of them live. People often collect them for ornaments. Sometimes you may be lucky enough to find the living animals scuttling around on the bottom of a lower-shore sandy pool.

*I-Spy for* ***15***

**Mermaid's purse**

Nothing at all to do with mermaids but actually the egg-case of one of any of the small species of shark that live around our coasts. The little strings at the end help to anchor the mermaid's purse to seaweeds but sometimes they come free and are washed up on the shore.

*I-Spy for* ***20***

**Cuttlefish bone**

Cuttlefishes are relatives of winkles and mussels, and the 'bone' is an internal supporting structure, the cuttlefish's equivalent of a shell. Living cuttlefishes are not often seen because most of them live in deeper water below the low-tide line but 'bones' from dead animals are often washed up on the shore.

*I-Spy for* ***15***

**Sea potato**
The sea potato is not a vegetable but a relative of the starfish. It is actually a type of sea urchin. Sea potatoes normally live beneath the sand but, in rough weather, they may occasionally become stranded on the surface, and you will find them when the tide is out.
*I-Spy for **20***

**Ripples in the sand**
As the tide goes out, the action of the waves often leaves a series of undulating ripples in the surface of the sand. These may remain full of water for a time and, if you look carefully, you may find tiny shrimps and other creatures in them.
*I-Spy for **10***

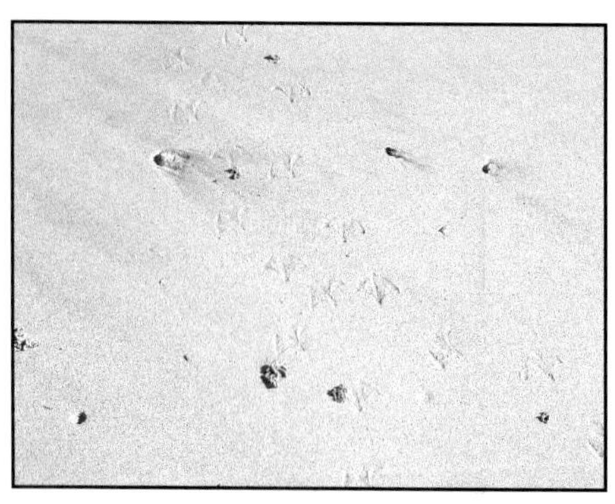

**Bird footprints in the sand**
As birds, such as gulls, walk around on the sand, their feet sink into it leaving distinctive marks. Gull footprints, such as those shown here, show the marks of the webs between the toes. If there are no webs, the footprints are likely to be those of one of the waders, such as the oystercatcher.
*I-Spy for **10***

**Fulmar**
You are most likely to see this relative of the albatross where there are cliffs close by. They nest on the cliffs and love gliding along the cliff-face, carried along on the breezes blowing in from the sea.
*I-Spy for **20***

**Lesser black-backed gull**
This gull may be found on almost any type of shore, or swimming on the sea. If you can get close to it you will see that it has yellow legs. Also look out for the bigger great black-backed gull with its pinkish, flesh-coloured legs.
*I-Spy for **15***

**Herring gull**
This is the commonest of our gulls and is found all around the coast. In recent years they have become a problem for they are very bold and will fly down and steal the sandwiches from the hands of holidaymakers. The herring gull's main food is herrings. True or false?

*I-Spy for **5***
*Double with answer and double again if you see a notice advising not to feed the gulls*

### Shag and cormorant

Both these birds are common around our coasts and are not easy to tell apart. The photograph is of a shag which nests on sea cliffs and is almost always seen off the coast. The cormorant is a little bigger and has a white throat and white wing patches. It is more often seen around estuaries and inland waters.

*I-Spy **15** for each*

### Terns

You are most likely to see terns diving for fish just offshore. They are streamlined birds with long tails, rather like swallows, and are sometimes called 'sea swallows'. You are most likely to see the common tern, (the one in the photograph), the similar Arctic tern, and the bigger, noisy Sandwich tern.

*I-Spy **20** for each of the three species*

**Guillemot**
Look out for the guillemot, and its close relative the razorbill, where there are plenty of high cliffs to provide nesting ledges. You can easily recognize these birds in flight for they have short wings and a very rapid wingbeat.
*I-Spy **20** each for the guillemot and razorbill*

**Shelduck**
This handsome duck is most often to be seen waddling around on the vast expanses of mud along the edges of large estuaries, though you may sometimes see it swimming on the sea off the coast.
*I-Spy for **20***

**Dunlin**
The dunlin is one of the group of birds generally known as waders. Dunlins can be seen running around the edge of the sea at almost any kind of shore where they dig into sand and mud for small sea creatures such as shrimps. They often form flocks containing hundreds or even thousands of birds.
*I-Spy **15** for any kind of wading bird – double if you are sure it is a dunlin*

# INDEX



**ANSWERS**

Title page: Two equal red and yellow horizontal bands: Red encrusting seaweeds: Ten; Five. Breadcrumb sponge: They are animals. Common starfish: True. Swimming crab: Its back legs are paddle shaped at the ends. Snakelocks anemone: The tentacles of the snakelocks cannot be withdrawn into the body. Common blenny: True. Herring gull: False, herring gulls are not particularly good at catching fish.




ISBN 1 85671 222 2

Michelin Tyre Public Limited Company
Edward Hyde Building, 38 Clarendon Road, Watford, Herts WD1 1SX





A CIP record for this title is available from the British Library.

Edited by Neil Curtis. Designed by Richard Garratt.

The Publisher gratefully acknowledges the contribution of Premaphotos Wildlife who provided all of the photographs in this book, and Rod Preston-Mafham who compiled the text.

Colour reproduction by Anglia Colour Ltd.